CREATED BY DIL.

WRITES AND DEVELOPS MANGA
PLOTS WHILE IN FEAR THAT
PANDAS MAY ONE DAY, RUN THE
PLANET.

ASKHAM BRYAN
COLLEGE
LEARNING RESOURCES

DEMON PRINCE - CHILDREN OF GAIA VOL. 1
CREATED BY DIL

STORYWRITER - DIL
ARTIST - PHILIP KNOTT
LETTERER AND EDITOR - DIPS

C.F.O - SUBODH DHANDA
C.E.O - DIL

PUBLISHED BY DIMENSIONAL MANGA
PO BOX 5087
WOLVERHAMPTON
WV1 9GY

VISIT OUR WEBSITE AT WWW.DIMENSIONALMANGA.COM

FIRST PRINT, 2008 JANUARY.

FIRST EDITION. COPYRIGHT © 2008. COPYRIGHT IN THESE
MATERIALS OR ANY PART OF THEM IS THE EXCLUSIVE
PROPERTY OF DIL/FIFTH DIMENSION LIMITED TRADING AS
DIMENSIONAL MANGA. ALL RIGHTS RESERVED. ALL COPYING,
RENTING, LENDING, TRANSMISSION AND/OR DIFFUSION OF
THESE MATERIALS OR ANY PART OF THEM IN ANY FORM OR BY
ANY MEANS IS STRICTLY PROHIBITED, WITHOUT THE PRIOR
WRITTEN PERMISSION FROM THE COPYRIGHT HOLDERS.

THIS MANGA IS A WORK OF FICTION. IT IS ENTIRELY
COINCIDENTAL IF IT BEARS ANY RESEMBLANCE TO ACTUAL
EVENTS, SCENARIOS OR PERSONS LIVING OR DEAD.

ISBN 978-0-9556274-0-8

PRINTED IN HONG KONG.

PARENTAL ADVISORY
RATED TEEN
Recommended for early to mid-
teens. May contain violence,
profanity and suggestive situations.

Knowledge is power.

Working hard isn't enough. Working
smart isn't enough. Doing whatever
it takes isn't enough, if you are using
the wrong layer of information to
begin with...

Knowledge is power over you.

DEMON PRINCE

CHILDREN OF GAIA

VOLUME 1

DEMON PRINCE CHILDREN OF GAIA

VOL. 1

CONTENTS

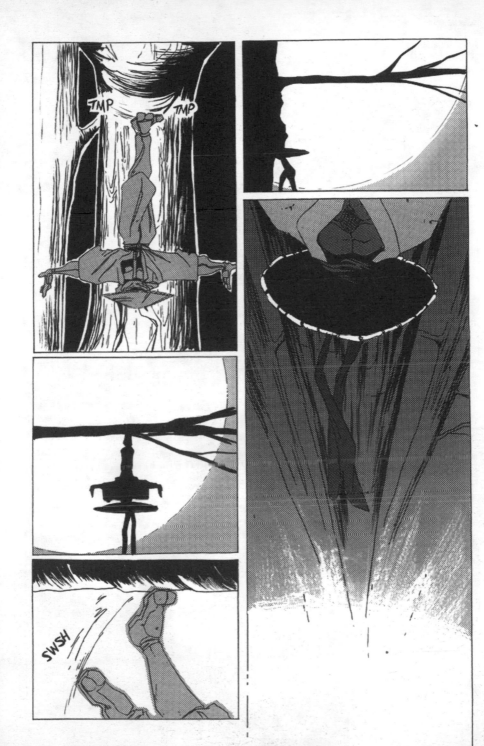

GRASP.

FWOOM!

BLACK DRAGON ARMY?

KAIZER'S MEN?

YA KNOW, I CAN'T SEE WHY WE STILL PATROL THIS AREA, THAT TREATY WAS SIGNED YEARS AGO WITHOUT ANY INCIDENTS PASSING.

WE MAY SEE YOU NEXT PATROL NIGHT, GUYS.

I THINK YOU SHOULD TELL KAIZER WE WON'T CROSS THE BORDER.

YEAH WELL, WE DON'T NORMALLY COME OUT THIS FAR.

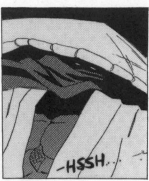

-HSSH...

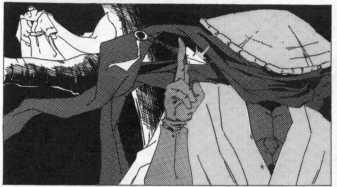

HE ALREADY KNEW I WAS GOING TO BE HERE?

CHAK

HUH?! THAT SHURIKEN WASN'T SUPPOSED TO KILL ME...?

WHAT'S HE UP TO?

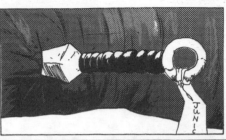

Chapter 2

KRUK!

WHY YOU!!!!

SHUN GET MOVING! IF IT IS A WAR KAIZER WANTS, THEN...

A BLACK DRAGON SOLDIER?!! THIS ISN'T RIGHT..

NOW... STOP FOOLING AROUND AND GO!!!

HE'S GOT IT!

REALISE, THAT WHAT YOU HOLD IN YOUR HANDS IS THE KEY FOR THE FUTURE... A "PURE" FUTURE.

VASH!

WHATEVER COMES OF THIS, YOU MUST TAKE YOUR RIGHTFUL PLACE. IT'S WHAT I'VE FOUGHT FOR AND 'SHAPED'.

I'VE DEALT WITH BIGGER TROUBLE THAN KAIZER.

HUH?

DAD!? YOU ACT AS THOUGH YOU'RE NOT COMING BACK! MOM!? TELL HIM.

COME BACK IN PEACE... SETTLE THIS AS YOU DID BEFORE.

THIS ONLY CONCERNS KAIZER AND I!

REN, YOUR FATHER HAS ALWAYS BEEN STUBBORN, BUT THAT'S THE REASON HE GETS THINGS DONE.

ONCE AND FOR ALL... I'VE SAT BACK TOO LONG.

I WILL SETTLE THIS...

COME ON FATHER!

THE WOUND...? DRAKONS?

HUH?! THE SHURIKEN IS... DEVOURING... SHUN!

SHUN? SHUN? NOOOO! I THOUGHT THE FEUD HAD ENDED LONG AFTER 'THE DEMON PRINCE'...

THIS IS THE FINAL STRAW... KAIZER... YOU... WILL... PAY!!!

NO... IT CAN'T BE...

38

CUT THAT BASTARD DOWN! I WANT EVERY LAST BLACK DRAGON... DEAD!!!

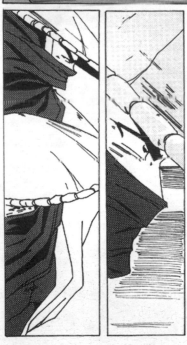

45

GA-DA-
THUD!

WHY
DANZAIVER...
WOULD YOU
ATTACK ME?!
WE'VE HAD
PARTNERSHIP
FOR YEARS!

K
A
I
Z
E
R

Chapter
3

61

HA-OOOOO

DING!

DING!

I'LL DO IT MYSELF... REIKEN, PLEASE...

CLICK!

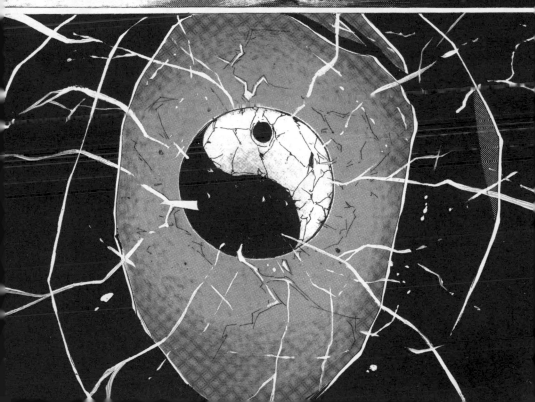

ALWAYS THE STUBBORN ONE EH? DANZAIVER? YOU OWE ME ONE.

IF I DIDN'T HAVE TO DEAL WITH THIS, I'D KILL YOU INSTEAD!

SHF

WHAT WAS THAT ATTACK DAD WAS JUST TRYING?

65

HMM... BEFORE I GO 'HOME'... I HAVE AN APPOINTMENT TO KEEP FIRST!

DO WHAT YOU LIKE WITH ME!!!

BESIDES, IT'S NOT WHAT I DO TO YOU...

BA-DUM

BA-DUM

SEE.

BA-DUM

BA-DUM

WE SHALL...

SHUT IT! OR DO YOU WANT US BOTH KILLED?!

DAD!!!

OUCH..

WE CAN'T DO ANYTHING ANYWAY, IT MAKES NO DIFFERENCE.

SO WHY DID I GET SPARED?!

I DON'T CARE, HE CAN KILL US ANYWAY IF HE WANTED TO.

WILL YOU SHUT UP?! WE NEED TO SEE WHERE THEY ARE GOING!

WILL YOU SHUT YOUR MOUTH! WE NEED TO SEE..

IT'S A DREAM.. A NIGHTMARE!! I WILL WAKE UP! LET'S SEE WHAT ELSE IS IN OUR DREAMS...

WHAT COULD BE IN THAT CAVE?

RUMBLE

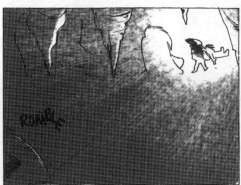

RUMBLE

REIKEN, GET THE DRAGON ORB.

WHAT DO WE HAVE HERE...

74

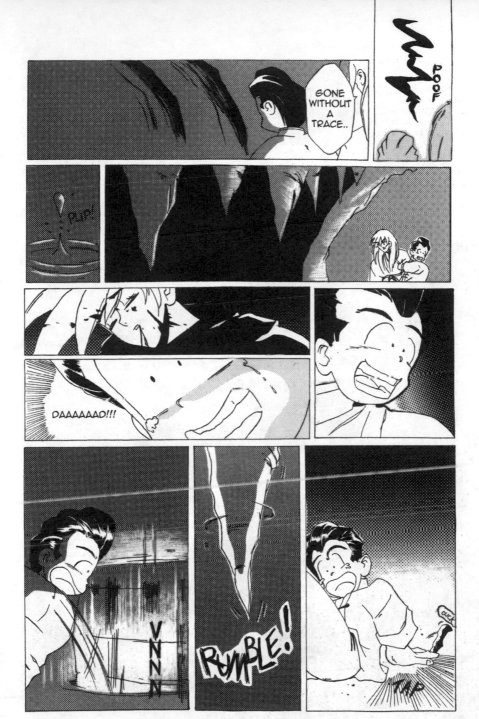

TO HELL WITH EVERYTHING! THEY'RE ALL GONE!!

WE'VE BOTH SUFFERED. SO MANY BAD THINGS CAN'T HAPPEN IN REAL LIFE?!!

THIS IS JUST A DREAM! A NIGHTMARE!

WAAAH, WAAAH!!

MATCHING TOO?

THAT AMULET IS THE SAME AS MINE! HAND IT OVER.

THIS CAN'T BE HAPPENING...

SHUU!!

WHAT COULD THIS BE ABOUT? THE AMULET LINKS!

MASTER... DRAKON HAS BEEN FREED AND THE ORB HAS BEEN TAKEN TOO. I CAN'T HELP BUT FEEL SOMETHING BAD COMING OUT OF THIS...

GARUDA'S RESPONSIBLE FOR THIS..

THIS ONE MUST BE LEFT TO THEM...

REALIZE, THERE'S ONLY SO MUCH YOU CAN DO. YOU'VE ALREADY DONE ENOUGH..

INTERFERENCE AT THIS STAGE IS NOT AN OPTION..

Chapter 4

SEEING MASTER WAS FUN.

YEAH..

YOU ALRIGHT?

YOU MEAN YOU'VE SEEN THEM BEFORE? WHY DIDN'T YOU SPEAK TO MASTER ABOUT THIS?

...LET'S SEE WHAT THE REST OF THE GROUP THINK.

IF ONLY MASTER REN WAS ALIVE..

THE VISIONS I'VE BEEN GETTING LATELY ARE JUST TOO REAL FOR ME TO IGNORE NOW.

MY QUEST IS TO SHOW THE WORLD WHAT IS POSSIBLE BY PUSHING MYSELF TO THE VERY LIMITS OF MY BEING. BUT THEN, WHAT IS THE LIMIT? IS IT A TEST UPON WHAT OTHERS HAVE ALREADY DONE? OR RATHER, WHAT'S YET TO BE SEEN? THAT IS THE QUEST I NOW FOLLOW.

REN, LIKE MYSELF, MASTERED THE ARTS IN ORDER TO PASS DOWN TO LATER GENERATIONS. THIS IS WHAT LIFE IS TRULY ABOUT.

IT WAS MYSTERIOUS, IS ALL I CAN SAY..

YOU KNOW I WASN'T AROUND WHEN MASTER REN PASSED ON. I NEVER KNEW WHAT HAPPENED.

93

105

PLAYING WITH YOU ALL SHOULD PROVE INTERESTING.

118

119

-VASH-

AKIRA!!!

YOU READY FOR THIS..

FIZZLE

SHH

SHH

SHMMMMM

LET'S SEE NOW.

HEH! AT LEAST MINE REACHED THE TARGET!

HMMM'M

?!

HEH! GEEZ, YOU'RE A FUNNY GUY!

KZZT

KZZT

I DON'T GET THIS.

122

...WHY WOULD HE JUST STAND THERE?

THIS ISN'T IT, I KNOW IT!

125

SHHH!
WE DON'T
WANT TO
GIVE
OURSELVES
AWAY..

KOFF KOFF

KOFF

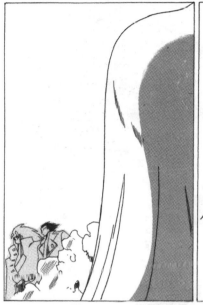

WELL,
AT
LEAST
NOT
NOW
ANYWAY.

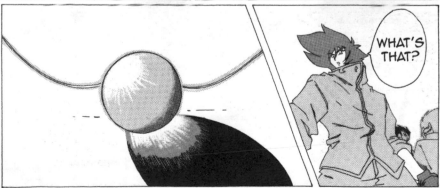

WHAT'S
THAT?

HEY, WE CAN'T MOVE!!

HAHA! I CHARGED ALL OF YOUR ENERGETIC ATTACKS INTO THIS ENERGETIC SPHERE.

THE SPHERE HAS DEATH READY FOR ONE OF YOU TO EXPERIENCE, BUT WHICH ONE? I'LL LET IT DECIDE.

YOU WON'T BE ABLE TO ESCAPE. I USED THE SMOKE LEFT BEHIND FROM YOUR ATTACKS TO HIDE, THEN I MADE SURE TO TIE YOU ALL ENERGETICALLY WHILE YOU COULDN'T SEE. SEE?! HA HAAA HA!

127

DAMN THIS GUY!

UNGH!

WE'VE GOT TO GET OUT OF THIS... COME ON!

KRCH..

LOOKING AT GENKAI GIVES ME STRENGTH.

HIS CALMNESS IN ALL SITUATIONS IS WHAT HAS ALWAYS KEPT ME GOING.

I KNOW NONE OF US WILL DIE TODAY. I CAN COUNT ON THAT!!

I BELIEVE IN GENKAI... EVEN WHEN THINGS ARE TOUGH...

ONLY ONE LEFT! HAHAHA! I WONDER WHAT?! MWHAHAHA!

134

EXPERIENCE WHAT MOMENTS YOU HAVE LEFT IN THIS PHYSICAL CONTAINER, EXPERIENCE IT WELL! IT'S WHAT LIFE'S ABOUT.

HIIYAAA...

HOW CAN HE BE SO BRAVE?... AKIRA..

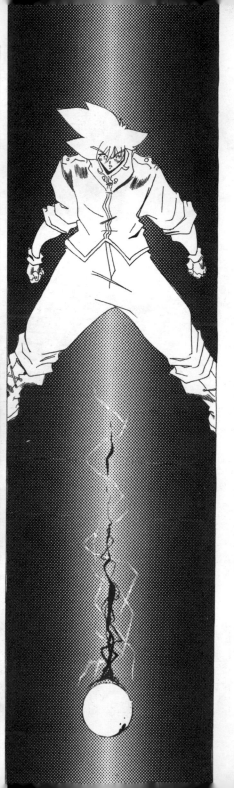

136

138

MASTER GAIA TOLD ME TO STAY HIDDEN AND JUST OBSERVE.

THERE'S NOTHING I CAN DO TO HIM ANYWAY, I'M OUTCLASSED.. WHAT IS GOING ON HERE?

HE ALSO TOLD ME TO STAY OUT OF HIS WAY.

Chapter 6

144

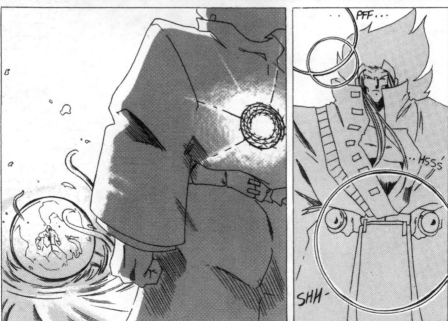

153

155

I'VE BEEN GETTING THESE VISIONS TOO. MASTER REN SAID SOMETHING ABOUT THAT IN THE PAST. IT SEEMS TO BE ALL ADDING UP TO WHAT HE WAS SAYING. I'LL BE MEETING MASTER WASABI IN A WHILE. SEE WHAT HE HAS TO SAY ABOUT IT.

MASTER WASABI WANTS US ALL TO MEET HIM TOMORROW. I WANT ALL OF YOU GUYS THERE...

SHH, IT'S OUR SECRET.

YOU COULD ALWAYS SHOW AKIRA YOUR SKILLS, AND TETSUO. LET'S ALL MEET IN THE USUAL PLACE.

FOR ME PLEASE.. MASTER REN WOULD HAVE WANTED US BOTH TO GO. OUR SECRETS SHOULD BE SHARED WITH THE WORLD, NOT KEPT BY OURSELVES. YOU KNOW IT'S WHAT MASTER REN WOULD SAY.

I DON'T SEE WHY WE SHOULD MEET TOMORROW. EIJI, HE ISN'T OUR MASTER. IF ANYTHING, TETSUO AND AKIRA SHOULD GO BY THEMSELVES. THEY'RE HIS STUDENTS! HEH!!

158

159

OH. I ALMOST FORGOT..

POP

SHYAA!

-FSH-

KI YAAAOOO

I'LL BE BACK FOR YOU, LATER.

TOMORROW SHOULD BE INTERESTING...

162

163

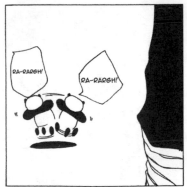

164

HEHE.. ZZZZ.

DROP

NOT SO... FAST?

COME HERE! GOT YA!

ZZZZZ Z Z Z Z Z

HMM, VERY STRANGE.. THE THIRD DEMON PRINCE CYCLE SEEMS ODD.. IT'S NOT EVEN BEGUN. SOMETHING'S NOT FEELING RIGHT ABOUT THIS...

RA-RARGH!

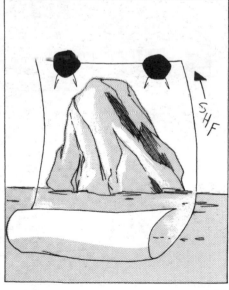

The journey from here on in really begins, unfolding in possibilities, shifting up several levels and layers beyond what you think you've 'seen'.
Be sure to join us for the next exciting graphic novel of Demon Prince: Children of Ga

TO BE CONTINUED...

DEMON PRINCE™

CHILDREN OF GAIA

Vol.2
Coming soon!
Check website for release updates!

WWW.DIMENSIONALMANGA.COM

Demon Prince:Children of Gaia © 2008 By Dil/Fifth Dimension Ltd trading as Dimensional Manga.

DIMENSIONAL MANGA ™

ONLINE STORE

POSTERS

EXCLUSIVE DOWNLOADS

COMIC PREVIEWS

AND MORE...

WWW.DIMENSIONALMANGA.COM

Demon Prince:Children of Gaia © 2008 By Dil/Fifth Dimension Ltd trading as Dimensional Manga.

DEMON PRINCE ™
CHILDREN OF GAIA
ART COLLECTORS BOOK.

COMING SOON!

GENKAI

JUNICHI

ONLINE STORE

GET YOUR MOBILE ACTION!

WWW.DIMENSIONALMANGA.COM

Demon Prince:Children of Gaia © 2008 By Dil/Fifth Dimension Ltd trading as Dimensional Manga.

All pictures are full colour.

SMS:

 SMS GET DRAKON1 to 60999

 SMS GET DRAKON1 to 19911119

Rest of the world, visit -
WWW.DIMENSIONALMANGA.COM

£2.00

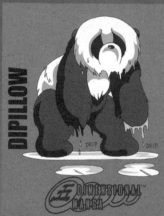

 SMS GET DPILLOW to 60999

 SMS GET DPILLOW to 19911119

Rest of the world, visit -
WWW.DIMENSIONALMANGA.COM

£2.00

EXCLUSIVE COLLECTABLE
CELL PHONE CONTENT!

WWW.DIMENSIONALMANGA.COM

*Ask bill payers permission before claiming your exclusive collectables.
*All images do not represent final quality that you will recieve.
*UK mobile phone networks include: O2, Vodafone, Tmobile, Orange and Three.
*Australian networks include Telstra, Optus and Vodafone.

Demon Prince:Children of Gaia © 2008 By Dil/Fifth Dimension Ltd trading as Dimensional Manga.

All pictures are full colour.
SMS:

 SMS GET GENKAI5 to 60999

 SMS GET GENKAI5 to 19911119

Rest of the world, visit -
WWW.DIMENSIONALMANGA.COM

£2.00

 SMS GET EIJI1 to 60999

 SMS GET EIJI1 to 19911119

Rest of the world, visit -
WWW.DIMENSIONALMANGA.COM

£2.00

EXCLUSIVE ALTERNATIVE COLOURS
AVAILABLE ONLY ON OUR WEBSITE!

WWW.DIMENSIONALMANGA.COM

*Ask bill payers permission before claiming your exclusive collectables.
*All images do not represent final quality that you will recieve.
*UK mobile phone networks include: O2, Vodafone, Tmobile, Orange and Three.
*Australian networks include Telstra, Optus and Vodafone.

Demon Prince:Children of Gaia © 2008 By Dil/Fifth Dimension Ltd trading as Dimensional Manga.

All pictures are full colour.

SMS:

 SMS GET AKIRA1 to 60999

 SMS GET AKIRA1 to 19911119

Rest of the world, visit -
WWW.DIMENSIONALMANGA.COM

£2.00

 SMS GET TETSUO5 to 60999

 SMS GET TETSUO5 to 19911119

Rest of the world, visit -
WWW.DIMENSIONALMANGA.COM

£2.00

ALTERNATE PICTURES FOR YOUR FAVOURITE CHARACTERS AVAILABLE!

WWW.DIMENSIONALMANGA.COM

*Ask bill payers permission before claiming your exclusive collectables.
*All images do not represent final quality that you will recieve.
*UK mobile phone networks include: O2, Vodafone, Tmobile, Orange and Three.
*Australian networks include Telstra, Optus and Vodafone.

Demon Prince:Children of Gaia © 2008 By Dil/Fifth Dimension Ltd trading as Dimensional Manga.

All pictures are full colour.

SMS:

 SMS GET KO1 to 60999

 SMS GET KO1 to 19911119

Rest of the world, visit -
WWW.DIMENSIONALMANGA.COM

£2.00

 SMS GET SHUN5 to 60999

 SMS GET SHUN5 to 19911119

Rest of the world, visit -
WWW.DIMENSIONALMANGA.COM

£2.00

SEE OUR EVER GROWING LIST OF
PICTURES AND IMAGES FOR YOU TO GET!

WWW.DIMENSIONALMANGA.COM

*Ask bill payers permission before claiming your exclusive collectables.
*All images do not represent final quality that you will recieve.
*UK mobile phone networks include: O2, Vodafone, Tmobile, Orange and Three.
*Australian networks include Telstra, Optus and Vodafone.

Demon Prince:Children of Gaia © 2008 By Dil/Fifth Dimension Ltd trading as Dimensional Manga.

All pictures are full colour.

SMS:

 SMS GET GAIA5 to 60999

 SMS GET GAIA5 to 19911119

Rest of the world, visit -
WWW.DIMENSIONALMANGA.COM

£2.00

 SMS GET GARUD to 60999

 SMS GET GARUD to 19911119

Rest of the world, visit -
WWW.DIMENSIONALMANGA.COM

£2.00

WWW.DIMENSIONALMANGA.COM

*Ask bill payers permission before claiming your exclusive collectables.
*All images do not represent final quality that you will recieve.
*UK mobile phone networks include: O2, Vodafone, Tmobile, Orange and Three.
*Australian networks include Telstra, Optus and Vodafone.

Demon Prince:Children of Gaia © 2008 By Dil/Fifth Dimension Ltd trading as Dimensional Manga.

All pictures are full colour.

SMS:

 SMS GET REIJIN1 to 60999

 SMS GET REIJIN1 to 19911119

Rest of the world, visit -
WWW.DIMENSIONALMANGA.COM

£2.00

 SMS GET REIKEN1 to 60999

 SMS GET REIKEN1 to 19911119

Rest of the world, visit -
WWW.DIMENSIONALMANGA.COM

£2.00

WWW.DIMENSIONALMANGA.COM

*Ask bill payers permission before claiming your exclusive collectables.
*All images do not represent final quality that you will recieve.
*UK mobile phone networks include: O2, Vodafone, Tmobile, Orange and Three.
*Australian networks include Telstra, Optus and Vodafone.

Demon Prince:Children of Gaia © 2008 By Dil/Fifth Dimension Ltd trading as Dimensional Manga.

All pictures are full colour.

SMS:

 SMS GET KANB to 60999

 SMS GET KANB to 19911119

Rest of the world, visit -
WWW.DIMENSIONALMANGA.COM

£2.00

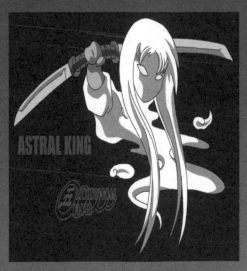

 SMS GET AK1 to 60999

 SMS GET AK1 to 19911119

Rest of the world, visit -
WWW.DIMENSIONALMANGA.COM

£2.00

WWW.DIMENSIONALMANGA.COM

*Ask bill payers permission before claiming your exclusive collectables.
*All images do not represent final quality that you will recieve.
*UK mobile phone networks include: O2, Vodafone, Tmobile, Orange and Three.
*Australian networks include Telstra, Optus and Vodafone.

Demon Prince:Children of Gaia © 2008 By Dil/Fifth Dimension Ltd trading as Dimensional Manga.

All pictures are full colour.
SMS:

 SMS GET LUCIFER1 to
60999

 SMS GET LUCIFER1 to
19911119

Rest of the world, visit -
WWW.DIMENSIONALMANGA.COM

£2.00

WWW.DIMENSIONALMANGA.COM

*Ask bill payers permission before claiming your exclusive collectables.
*All images do not represent final quality that you will recieve.
*UK mobile phone networks include: O2, Vodafone, Tmobile, Orange and Three.
*Australian networks include Telstra, Optus and Vodafone.

Demon Prince:Children of Gaia © 2008 By Dil/Fifth Dimension Ltd trading as Dimensional Manga.

A MESSAGE FROM THE CREATOR, DIL.

I'D LIKE TO TAKE THIS SPACE TO DEDICATE MY APPRECIATION TO SEVERAL PEOPLE, WHO HAVE MADE THIS DREAM A REALITY.

DIPS (AKA FINALDIPS AND ALL OF THE OTHER PANDAS NAMED AND MODELLED AFTER HIM), WHOSE BELIEF IN ME WAS UNSHAKABLE AND PIVOTAL WITH MY DECISION TO DO THIS. DIPS DOING THIS, IS WHY THE PROJECT WAS BORN. I CAN'T THANK HIM ENOUGH!

SUBODH FOR ALL HIS HELP AND DEDICATION TOWARDS THE PROJECT AS A WHOLE AND FOR ALL THE SUPPORT HE HAS GIVEN.

I'D ALSO LIKE TO SAY THAT I'M PRIVELAGED TO WORK WITH AN ARTIST WHO CARES SOLELY ABOUT THE WORK. HIS WILLINGNESS TO GO BEYOND HIS DUTY IS A QUALITY RARE TO FIND, PHIL.

FINALLY I'D LIKE TO THANK NEIL TURNER (A VERY GOOD FRIEND) FOR ALL HIS ENTHUSIASM AND ENERGY TOWARDS THE PROJECT.

AND OF COURSE YOU!